ROAD TO REVOLUTION!

ROAD TO REVOLUTION!

Stan Mack and Susan Champlin

SCHOLASTIC INC.
New York Toronto London Auckland
Sydney New Delhi Hong Kong

Typeset in CCFaceFont
Art created with Pigma Micron pen and Pelikan watercolor on 1-ply Strathmore paper.
Book design by Stan Mack, Susan Champlin, and Yelena Safronova.

Copyright © 2009 by Stan Mack and Susan Champlin.
All rights reserved. Published by Scholastic Inc., 557 Broadway, New York, NY 10012,
by arrangement with Bloomsbury U.S.A. Children's Books.
Printed in the U.S.A.

ISBN-13: 978-0-545-32815-9
ISBN-10: 0-545-32815-2

10   40   20 19 18

To Sarah and Noah
—S. M.

To Annie, my own model of teenage ingenuity
—S. C.

PROLOGUE

IN WHICH WE LEARN HOW WE GOT HERE

Boston, 1775. Tension has been building for years between the American colonies and their mother country, England. Now they are on the brink of war—and the most likely place for it to start is the town of Boston, in the Massachusetts Bay Colony.

England boasts the mightiest military in the world and rules a sprawling trading empire of colonies that circle the globe. England lets her American colonies govern themselves on local matters but controls their lives in almost every other way: regulating their businesses, taxing their imports and exports, boarding their ships without permission—while ignoring the colonists' complaints.

The British rulers—King George III and Parliament—commit a series of blunders that ultimately provoke these once-loyal subjects into outright defiance.

Beginning in 1764, Parliament imposes three new taxes on the colonists—first on sugar and molasses (the Sugar Act, 1764); then on printed materials, including newspapers, legal documents, and even playing cards, requiring them to display a special British stamp (the Stamp Act, 1765); and then on lead, glass, paint, paper, and tea (the Townshend Acts, 1767).

These taxes make the colonists furious, especially because they have no say in Parliament—in other words, no say in making the laws that affect them. "No taxation without representation!" becomes their rallying cry, and the thirteen argumentative colonies unite against a common enemy. They protest by threatening tax officials, by boycotting English goods, and by rioting in the streets. The most extreme protests come from the rebels in Boston, led by talented troublemakers Samuel Adams, John Hancock, and Dr. Joseph Warren. Because of the riots, Parliament decides in 1768 to send British soldiers to Boston to keep the peace. Then things *really* heat up.

1

1770: British soldiers with guns come face-to-face with a mob of citizens who hit them with snowballs, chunks of ice, and wooden clubs. The soldiers fire on the crowd, killing five people. The "Boston Massacre" convinces the colonists that England will use military force to make the colonies submit.

1773: Parliament cancels (or "repeals") almost all the taxes—but, to show who's boss, keeps the tax on tea. To make matters worse, it gives the British East India Company total control of one of the biggest businesses in the colonies: the sale of tea. To protest, Samuel Adams organizes the rebels known as the Sons of Liberty, who disguise themselves as Indians, board British ships, and dump forty-five tons of tea into Boston Harbor. This becomes known as the Boston Tea Party. In retaliation, Parliament closes Boston's busy port, orders British general Thomas Gage to take control of the city, and announces that from now on, all important government officials in the colonies will be appointed by the British government. The colonies raise the stakes by forming illegal revolutionary committees to plot their next moves.

1774: In Philadelphia, representatives from all the colonies meet at the First Continental Congress. They declare that Parliament has no authority over the colonies—and that if force is used against Bostonians, all the colonies will come to their aid. (The Second Continental Congress is scheduled for the spring of 1775. Samuel Adams and John Hancock will attend.)

In Massachusetts, rebel leaders appoint a Committee of Safety, which begins storing up weapons and organizes special companies of minutemen to be ready to fight at a minute's notice. The committee meets secretly in Boston under the very nose of General Gage. It relays information on British troop movements to the rebels in the countryside.

At this time, Boston is almost an island—connected to the mainland by a skinny strip of land called Boston Neck. To get into or out of Boston, committee messengers must get past British guards. One of the most resourceful and reliable messengers is Paul Revere.

Meanwhile, General Gage is being pressured by Parliament to arrest the radical leaders, send his soldiers into the countryside, and destroy the fledgling rebellion!

In this book, you'll meet fictional characters who get caught up with real-life people and events. After reading our story, please turn to the epilogue, in the back. There, you'll find out what's fact and what's fiction.

THE MAIN CHARACTERS

BRITISH MILITARY "THE REGULARS"

Better known by the Bostonians as redcoats and lobsterbacks because of their red uniforms.

TORIES

Colonists who remain loyal to England and fear the growing rebellion.

SAMUEL ADAMS & DR. JOSEPH WARREN

Two of the most important leaders of the Boston rebellion.

AVERAGE BOSTONIANS

Citizens suffering from the British occupation of Boston.

PAUL REVERE

Silversmith and radical (a colonist driven to extreme action by British oppression).

MINUTEMEN

Rebel militia soldiers trained to respond quickly to a British attack.

NICK

An orphan who lives by his wits on the streets of Boston.

PENELOPE BROWN (Penny)

Daughter of the owner of a local tavern— the One-Eyed Fox.

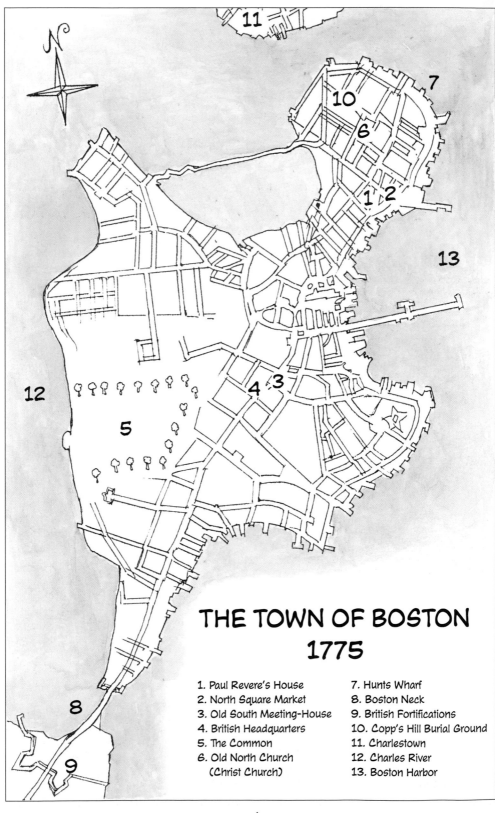

THE TOWN OF BOSTON
1775

1. Paul Revere's House
2. North Square Market
3. Old South Meeting-House
4. British Headquarters
5. The Common
6. Old North Church
   (Christ Church)
7. Hunts Wharf
8. Boston Neck
9. British Fortifications
10. Copp's Hill Burial Ground
11. Charlestown
12. Charles River
13. Boston Harbor

CHAPTER 1

IN WHICH NICK KNOCKS PENNY FOR A LOOP

February 1775. Boston, North Square Market With the British blockading the port, only a trickle of food and supplies can get into Boston over Boston Neck. The citizens, except those wealthy Tories with ties to the British, are growing desperate.

SORRY, PENNY. I GOT CLEANED OUT THIS MORNING. ALL I HAVE IS THIS SCRAWNY RABBIT AND TWO POTATOES.

I'LL TAKE THE POTATOES.

HEH! A RICH TORY, RIPE FOR THE PLUCKING!

HA! EMPTY STOMACHS WILL TAKE THE FIGHT OUT OF THESE PEOPLE.

??? ! THAT BOY STOLE MY MONEY PURSE!

WHO IS HE?!

JUST A NAMELESS STREET URCHIN, SIR.

STOP, THIEF! SOMEBODY GRAB HIM, HE STOLE MY PURSE!

HE'LL NEVER CATCH NICK. NO ONE KNOWS THESE STREETS BETTER.

MR. SNOW, THAT BOY IS A THIEF.

NICK HAS BEEN KNOWN TO GO AFTER A FAT WALLET, BUT HE HAS A GOOD HEART.

HE'S AN ORPHAN. GROOMS THE BRITISH HORSES AT MULLIN'S STABLE FOR HIS KEEP. HE'S GOOD WITH ANIMALS.

HE SHOULD TRY PEOPLE.

Penny's route home takes her by the house of her best friend, Sarah Revere.

8

March 1775. Penny and Nick are back at the market, where a British supply wagon is stuck in the mud, much to the enjoyment of a few unemployed dockworkers.

13

14

15

CHAPTER 2

IN WHICH NICK TAKES A SWIG AND PENNY TAKES A SWING

IT'S A WINE AND ROOT CELLAR. I RUN ERRANDS FOR THE PEOPLE WHO OWN IT.

THIS IS EXCELLENT MADEIRA WINE. COMES ALL THE WAY FROM SPAIN, YOU KNOW.

PORTUGAL. MY DAD OWNS A TAVERN, SO I KNOW WHAT MADEIRA IS, THANK YOU.

AND I KNOW MY SKIRT IS A MESS AGAIN AND IT'S YOUR FAULT.

HEY, YOU'RE THE ONE WHO THREW THE FISH.

BUT YOU TIPPED OVER THE CART!

THOSE DOCK-WORKERS ARE MY FRIENDS. WHAT DID YOU EXPECT?

SO YOU'RE A REBEL AS WELL AS A THIEF.

A WHA—?!

I KNOW WHO YOU ARE. YOU'RE AN ORPHAN AND A PICKPOCKET— BUT YOU HAVE A GOOD HEART. SUPPOSEDLY.

AND I KNOW WHO YOU ARE—A PROPER GIRL WHO...

PROPER?! YOU TAKE THAT BACK!

...WHO GOT CARRIED AWAY BY MY GOOD LOOKS AND TRIED TO SAVE ME.

C'MON, LET'S GO.

UGH. MY SKIRT IS GETTING DIRTY—*AGAIN*.

SO GET YOUR FATHER TO GO TO THE STORE AND BUY YOU ANOTHER ONE.

THE SHOPS CARRY BRITISH GOODS, AND I WON'T BUY THEM. MY MOTHER AND I MADE THIS FROM HOMESPUN CLOTH.

WHY?

I REFUSE TO SUPPORT THE BRITISH. THEY BARGE INTO TOWN, FORCE PEOPLE TO HOUSE THEM, THEY THINK THEY *OWN* US!

OKAY, OKAY, YIKES. SORRY I ASKED.

SHOES · BOOT

CLOSED — NO BUCKLES DUE TO BLOCKADE

DON'T YOU CARE? AREN'T YOU *MAD* THAT THEY'VE TAKEN OVER OUR TOWN?

MY FRIENDS ON THE DOCK ARE OUT OF WORK. OTHERWISE IT DOESN'T AFFECT ME.

BUT THEY FILL OUR STREETS, TREAT US LIKE CHILDREN AND CRIMINALS.

UM, I *AM* A CRIMINAL.

19

20

STAY BACK! IT'S THOSE TWO SOLDIERS WHO WERE CHASING US.

OOF!

WHAT ARE THEY DOING?

THEY'RE LISTENING AT THE DOOR OF THE GREEN DRAGON.

BAM!

YOW! YOW!

?

HA! LOOK WHO'S HERE, OUR FAITHFUL BRITISH SHADOWS.

COME, SAMUEL, WE HAVE HANDBILLS TO DISTRIBUTE.

WHO'S THE RUMPLED OLD GOAT?

DON'T YOU KNOW ANYTHING? THAT'S SAMUEL ADAMS. YOU COULD TAKE TROUBLEMAKING LESSONS FROM HIM. THE BOSTON TEA PARTY WAS HIS IDEA.

WHO'S THE DANDY WITH HIM?

DANDY? THAT'S DR. JOSEPH WARREN. MR. REVERE SAYS HE'S THE BRAINS BEHIND THE BOSTON REBELLION.

THEY'RE COMING THIS WAY.

LAUGH NOW, ADAMS. KING GEORGE WILL SOON HAVE HIS BOOT ON YOUR NECK!

WE'RE TREMBLING WITH FEAR, AREN'T WE, SON?

Y-YES, SIR... I MEAN, NO, SIR!

THOSE TWO ARE PICKING A FIGHT WITH THE WHOLE BRITISH EMPIRE? I THINK THEY'LL NEED HELP.

FROM WHOM?

ME. A MAN OF ACTION.

AND THEN YOU WOKE UP.

?

LET'S SEE WHAT THEIR HANDBILL SAYS.

HMMPH! MORE TREASONOUS RANTINGS FROM ADAMS AND THE OTHER LUNATICS.

SOUNDS LIKE A GOOD TIME TO ARREST ALL THE RABBLE-ROUSERS AND HAVE DONE WITH IT.

ATTENTION!
BOSTON MASSACRE ANNIVERSARY
MARCH 6, 1775
COME AND HONOR THE
INNOCENT BOSTONIANS
BUTCHERED BY BRITISH
SOLDIERS ON MARCH 5, 1770.
OLD SOUTH MEETING-HOUSE
ORATION BY DR. JOSEPH WARREN

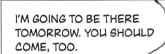

I'M GOING TO BE THERE TOMORROW. YOU SHOULD COME, TOO.

MAKE WAY!

RIFFRAFF!

HEY!

I'LL BE THERE.

THERE'S MY FATHER.

UM, I THINK I HEAR MY HORSES CALLING ME. I'D BETTER GO.

BUTCHER

That night..

MY MOTHER AND BROTHER ARE FAR AWAY. MY FATHER SERVES THE BRITISH. THERE'S WAR TALK EVERYWHERE. WHERE'S THIS GOING TO LEAD?

And on the roof of Mullin's stable...

WHO GOES THERE?

TAKING OVER OUR TOWN!

DUTY TO REBEL!

HEADED FOR WAR!

25

CHAPTER 3

IN WHICH NICK AND PENNY FOIL A PLOT

March 6, 1775. Boston Massacre Anniversary, Old South Meeting-House.

NICK, YOU MADE IT!

LOOKS LIKE EVERY BRITISH-HATING BOSTONIAN IS HERE.

AND A WHOLE LOT OF ANGRY-LOOKING BRITISH OFFICERS.

LET'S GO UP TO THE GALLERY WHERE WE CAN SEE.

FOR THE ANNIVERSARY ORATION, I PRESENT DR. JOSEPH WARREN.

SAMUEL ADAMS, JOHN HANCOCK, AND THE OTHER REBEL LEADERS ARE UP FRONT.

WE HAVE AGAIN SEEN A BRITISH ARMY IN OUR LAND...

...AND THAT'LL BE THE SIGNAL FOR ALL OF US OFFICERS TO RUSH FORWARD AND ARREST ADAMS AND HANCOCK.

WATCH THIS.

...SENT TO ENFORCE OBEDIENCE TO ACTS OF PARLIAMENT DESTRUCTIVE OF OUR LIBERTY.

YOU ARE TO DECIDE THE IMPORTANT QUESTION...

...ON WHICH RESTS THE HAPPINESS AND LIBERTY OF MILLIONS YET UNBORN...

31

Later at Mullin's stable.

SO *NOW* YOU'RE A PATRIOT?

DON'T KNOW ABOUT THAT, BUT I LIKED WHAT HE SAID...

...AND I ACTUALLY SAVED ADAMS AND HANCOCK FROM ARREST.

WHAT DO YOU MEAN, "I"? WHO PERSUADED YOU TO GO HEAR DR. WARREN? WHO YELLED "FIRE"?

YEAH! YOU'RE ALWAYS GETTING ME INTO TROUBLE.

YOU MEAN *OUT* OF TROUBLE!

CHAPTER 4

IN WHICH NICK AND PENNY GET THE GOODS
ON THE BRITISH

April 14, 1775. Nick watches the British warship Somerset *move up the Charles River to block the water passage to Charlestown and prevent communication between the patriots of Boston and those in the countryside.*

April 15, 1775. Penny observes elite redcoat troops converging on North Square and on the huge open field that they use for maneuvers, called the Common.

April 16. Nick overhears a British spy reporting back from the countryside.

I SAW THE REBEL WEAPONS IN CONCORD MYSELF. AND I HEAR THAT THOSE TRAITORS ADAMS AND HANCOCK ARE HIDING OUT IN LEXINGTON ON THEIR WAY TO THAT ILLEGAL CONGRESS IN PHILADELPHIA.

GOOD WORK. REPORT TO GAGE AND THEN LET'S GO GET SOME RUM.

April 17. Penny listens to nervous townsfolk.

THE REDCOATS ARE READYING SOMETHING BIG, BUT WHERE?

HOW MANY SOLDIERS? HOW WILL THEY TRAVEL?

THE IMPORTANT QUESTION IS WHEN.

I HOPE DR. WARREN KNOWS MORE THAN WE DO.

April 18. Mullin's stable.

NICK, THIS GUESSING GAME IS MAKING PEOPLE CRAZY.

HERE COME TWO CUSTOMERS.

I'LL GET OUT OF SIGHT.

35

SADDLE OUR HORSES, BOY. CAMPAIGN SADDLES, NOT PARADE.

YESSIR.

FINALLY, GRANDMA GAGE HAS STOPPED DITHERING AND IS TAKING SOME ACTION!

?

I WISH I COULD SEE THE LOOK ON THE YOKELS' FACES WHEN THEY WAKE UP TOMORROW MORNING TO DISCOVER THAT...

...700 OF OUR FINEST SOLDIERS HAVE CROSSED THE CHARLES IN THE DEAD OF NIGHT, HAVE ARRESTED ADAMS AND HANCOCK IN LEXINGTON, AND ARE ON ROUTE TO CONCORD, WHERE...

...THEY WILL DESTROY THE REBELS' STOCKPILE OF WEAPONS—AND THEIR BIG-DEAL REBELLION ALONG WITH 'EM.

AND THE FOOLS AT CONCORD WON'T SUSPECT A THING BECAUSE WE'LL BE GUARDING THE ROADS TO MAKE SURE NO WARNING REACHES THEM.

SARAH REVERE'S FATHER KNOWS ME—HE'S ONE OF THE IMPORTANT PATRIOTS.

LET'S GO SEE HIM!

THE STREETS ARE FULL OF SOLDIERS. WE'LL STICK TO THE BACK ALLEYS.

SARAH!

WE NEED TO TALK TO YOUR DAD!

HE'S PROBABLY AT DR. WARREN'S...

...ON HANOVER STREET.

LET'S GO!

PENNY, IT'S DANGEROUS TO BE OUT...ESPECIALLY WITH THAT BOY. YOU'LL GET IN TROUBLE.

SHE ALREADY IS. WE ALL ARE.

April 18, 1775. Sundown.

HERE IT IS.

KNOCK KNOCK

YES?

DR. WARREN, WE HAVE INFORMATION... I HID BEHIND THE DOOR...DIDN'T KNOW WHO TO TELL...AT THE STABLE...BRITISH OFFICERS...CAMPAIGN SADDLES... ADAMS AND HANCOCK...THE WEAPONS AT CONCORD...

WHOA, WHOA. SLOW DOWN.

DR. WARREN, YOU HAVE TO LISTEN...

I KNOW THAT VOICE.

IT'S MY DAUGHTER! PENNY, WHAT ARE YOU DOING HERE?

FATHER! WHAT ARE *YOU* DOING HERE?

TALK INSIDE! THERE ARE SOLDIERS EVERYWHERE!

PENNY, I'M WORKING WITH DR. WARREN AND HIS COMMITTEE OF SAFETY. WE'RE IN AN EMERGENCY MEETING.

AND WHO ARE YOU, YOUNG MAN?

NICK, AT YOUR SERVICE. NEED ERRANDS RUN, BAD GUYS' POCKETS PICKED, I'M YOUR MAN.

SIR, WE OVERHEARD THE BRITISH PLANS!

QUICKLY, COME TELL US ALL ABOUT IT!

Penny and Nick tell the grim-faced men what the British officers said.

...AND THEN THEY RODE OFF.

AND WE RUSHED HERE!

I DON'T BELIEVE THEM. THEY'RE CHILDREN, AND CHILDREN MAKE UP STORIES.

I'LL VOUCH FOR MY DAUGHTER, DR. CHURCH!

I BELIEVE THEM, BENJAMIN. WHAT THEY SAY FITS WITH WHAT WE'VE SUSPECTED.

WE CAN'T AFFORD TO HESITATE. WE MUST PUT OUR EMERGENCY PLANS INTO ACTION IMMEDIATELY!

WE HAVE TO GET WORD OUT TO LEXINGTON, WARN THE MILITIA IN CONCORD, AND ALERT EVERYONE IN THE COUNTRYSIDE ALONG THE WAY THAT THE REDCOATS ARE COMING!

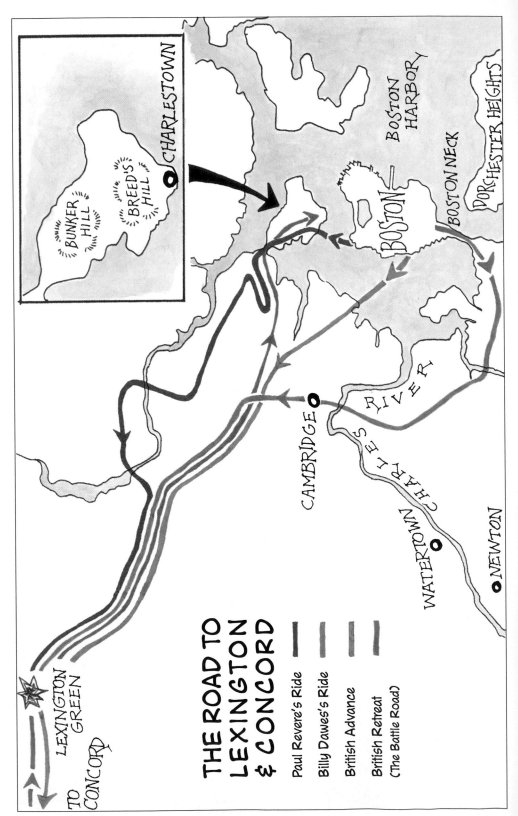

THE ROAD TO
LEXINGTON
& CONCORD

Paul Revere's Ride

Billy Dawes's Ride

British Advance

British Retreat
(The Battle Road)

LEXINGTON GREEN

TO CONCORD

CAMBRIDGE

WATERTOWN

NEWTON

CHARLES RIVER

BOSTON

BOSTON HARBOR

BOSTON NECK

DORCHESTER HEIGHTS

CHARLESTOWN

BUNKER HILL

BREED'S HILL

BILLY DAWES, YOU RIDE OUT BY THE NECK. IF ANYONE CAN FAKE HIS WAY PAST THE GUARDS, IT'S YOU.

YUP. YUP.

WILL BROWN, YOU GET REVERE'S BOAT AND TAKE IT TO HUNTS WHARF. THEN YOU'LL ROW HIM ACROSS TO CHARLESTOWN.

REVERE, FROM CHARLESTOWN, YOU WILL RIDE TO LEXINGTON AND CONCORD. WITH LUCK, YOU OR DAWES WILL GET BY ANY BRITISH SOLDIERS GUARDING THE ROUTE.

WHAT ABOUT YOU, WARREN?

IT'S TOO DANGEROUS HERE IN TOWN. TOMORROW I'LL LEAVE FOR CAMBRIDGE AND SET UP OUR HEADQUARTERS THERE.

FIRST, REVERE, YOU HAVE AN IMPORTANT TASK.

I'M READY!

AS FOR OUR TWO YOUNG FRIENDS...

MR. REVERE, WHATEVER YOU HAVE TO DO, I CAN HELP.

OH, YEAH? YOU HAVE A BIG MOUTH— LET'S SEE IF YOU CAN BACK IT UP. COME WITH ME.

DAD, I'M SORRY FOR WHAT I SAID ABOUT YOU AND THE BRITISH.

MY FAULT, PENNY. I THOUGHT I WAS PROTECTING YOU BY NOT TELLING YOU I WAS WORKING UNDERCOVER.

COME WITH ME. YOUR MOTHER WILL BE SO GLAD TO HAVE YOU WITH HER AGAIN.

April 18, 10 p.m.

GO IN SAFETY, MY FRIENDS.

WHERE ARE WE GOING, MR. REVERE?

TO MEET THE SEXTON OF OLD NORTH CHURCH.

SEXTON NEWMAN, YOU MADE IT!

'TWEREN'T EASY. I HAD TO CLIMB OUT A WINDOW AND OVER A ROOF TO AVOID THE REDCOATS.

ROBERT, THE BRITISH ARE ON THE MOVE. YOU MUST LIGHT *TWO* LAMPS.

WHO'S THE KID?

THIS IS NICK. PUT HIM TO WORK.

I MUST GO AND SAY GOODBYE TO MY FAMILY. NICK, WHEN YOU'RE DONE HERE, MEET ME AT THE WHARF.

WE'LL SEE HOW WELL YOU CAN ROW.

LET'S GO, KID.

FOLLOW ME—I HAVE THE KEYS TO THE CHURCH.

WE'RE GOING TO CARRY THESE TWO LANTERNS TO THE TOP OF THE STEEPLE AND LIGHT THEM WHERE THEY CAN BE SEEN ACROSS THE CHARLES RIVER.

IT'S THE SIGNAL TO ALERT OUR MEN WAITING IN CHARLESTOWN THAT THE BRITISH ARE ADVANCING BY WATER.

KNOCK KNOCK

YOU INSIDE, OPEN UP BY ORDER OF GENERAL GAGE!

COME OUT NOW, OR WE BREAK DOWN THE DOOR!

KID...

...TAKE THE LAMPS AND GO ON UP. I'LL DEAL WITH THEM. JUST FOLLOW THE STAIRS TO THE TOP.

IF I CAN'T GET RID OF THEM, YOU LIGHT BOTH LANTERNS AND HOLD THEM UP FACING CHARLESTOWN. KEEP THEM LIT FOR ONLY A MINUTE.

THEN COME BACK DOWN AND GET OUT FAST BY THE BACK WINDOW. GOOD LUCK—MUCH DEPENDS ON YOU.

OFFICERS, IT'S JUST ME, SEXTON NEWMAN, DOING CHURCH WORK.

IT'S AFTER CURFEW. LOCK UP RIGHT NOW, AND GO HOME.

Y-YESSIR!

CHAPTER 5

IN WHICH NICK LIGHTS THE WAY AND PENNY DONATES HER PETTICOAT

NOW TO GET OUT OF HERE.

April 18, 11 p.m., Hunts Wharf.

PENNY, I HATE TO SAY THIS, BUT YOU HAVE THE MAKINGS OF A FINE SPY.

LIKE FATHER, LIKE DAUGHTER.

REVERE, WE SAW THE LANTERN LIGHTS IN THE STEEPLE. GOOD WORK!

WASN'T ME, IT WAS NEWMAN AND NICK.

HERE COMES NICK NOW.

GOOD MAN, NICK! JUMP IN AND GRAB AN OAR. WE HAVE TO GET PAUL TO CHARLESTOWN.

ALL WE HAVE TO DO IS SLIP UNDER THE NOSES OF THE GUARDS ON THE SOMERSET.

WAIT! THEY'LL HEAR THE NOISE OF OUR OARLOCKS. WE NEED TO MUFFLE THE SOUND SOMEHOW.

SREEEK!

HERE, USE THIS...OOF.

MY PETTICOAT. I HATE WEARING IT ANYWAY.

RIP!

BETTER.

WE HAVE TO GO. JUMP IN, PENNY.

CHAPTER 6

IN WHICH NICK RIDES OLD MAGGIE TO BATTLE

REVERE?

YES, WITH WILL BROWN AND A YOUNG FRIEND, NICK.

WHEN WE SAW THE SIGNAL LIGHTS, WE SENT MESSENGERS TO LEXINGTON AND CONCORD.

THERE ARE BRITISH ADVANCE PATROLS EVERYWHERE. WE FEAR THE NEWS HASN'T GOTTEN THROUGH.

THIS HORSE WILL SERVE YOU WELL, REVERE.

THANKS TO ALL OF YOU.

NICK, DO WHAT YOU CAN TO WARN PEOPLE ALONG THE BACKROADS TO LEXINGTON.

I WILL, MR. REVERE.

IF I CAN BORROW A HORSE, I'LL RIDE SOUTH TO BRAINTREE, ALERT THE MILITIAS ALONG THE WAY, AND CHECK ON MY FAMILY.

WE HAVE ONE LEFT, WILL. YOU'RE WELCOME TO HIM.

I'M SORRY, WE DON'T HAVE ANY HORSES LEFT, NICK.

WHAT ABOUT THAT LITTLE ONE OVER THERE?

THAT'S JUST OLD MAGGIE. WE KEEP HER AROUND FOR CHILDREN TO RIDE—THOUGH IN HER TIME SHE WAS A GREAT JUMPER. YOU'RE WELCOME TO USE HER.

55

GOOD PEOPLE, MAGGIE.

GOOD CORN CAKES.

HALT! YOU ON THAT SILLY-LOOKING NAG!

HEY, IT'S THAT KID FROM THE STABLES! WHAT ARE YOU DOING HERE?

HE'S UP TO NO GOOD. YOU'RE COMING WITH US, BOY!

OF COURSE, SIR. I'M A LOYAL TORY, REMEMBER?

GET READY, MAGGIE.

NOW, MAGGIE...

...FLY!

HEY!

5 a.m. Nick arrives at Lexington Green.

REVERE AND DAWES WERE ALREADY HERE. THEY'VE GONE ON TO WARN THE MILITIA AT CONCORD.

AND ADAMS AND HANCOCK ARE SAFELY AWAY. THEY'RE ON THEIR WAY TO PHILADELPHIA.

BUCKMAN TAVERN

CAPTAIN PARKER HAS ORDERED OUR MINUTE-MEN TO GATHER ON THE GREEN, JUST IN CASE.

THE REDCOATS HAVE BEEN SPOTTED COMING UP THE ROAD—HUNDREDS OF THEM!

OUR MEN ARE BRAVE, BUT THEY'RE ONLY PART-TIME SOLDIERS, AND THERE ARE LESS THAN 80 OF THEM.

STABLE YOUR HORSE, YOUNG MAN, AND HELP ME GET CITIZENS OUT OF THE LINE OF FIRE.

HERE THEY COME!

MEN, THIS IS A SYMBOLIC STAND. IF THE BRITISH TAKE NO ACTION, YOU LET THEM PASS...

...BUT IF THEY MEAN TO HAVE A WAR, LET IT START HERE.

HOLD FIRE! HOLD RANKS!

Suddenly, a British officer charges forward.

DISPERSE, YOU VILLAINS. LAY DOWN YOUR ARMS!

WE'VE MADE OUR POINT. FALL OUT, MEN. IT WOULD BE FOOLHARDY TO FIGHT THE ENTIRE BRITISH ARMY.

WHEW! GLAD THAT'S OVER.

I'M NOT LEAVING.

59

BLAM!

SOMEONE FIRED! THIS WASN'T SUPPOSED TO HAPPEN. GET INSIDE THE TAVERN!

THE BRITISH ARE CHARGING AND SHOOTING!

BLAM BLAM BLAM

AGH!

AGH!

BLAM

STAY BACK! IT'S A MASSACRE!

BLAM BLAM BLAM

HELP ME.

HOLD ON.

61

Six hours later. Nick is still in Lexington, helping with the injured. Nine minutemen have died, eleven are wounded.

I HOPE ONE OF OUR MEN WAS ABLE TO WARN CONCORD BEFORE THE REDCOATS GOT THERE.

LISTEN! THEY'RE COMING BACK!

BLAM
BLAM

I'LL GET MY GUN!

British soldiers appear, running wildly chased by enraged farmers and townspeople who fight guerrilla-style—shooting from behind rocks, trees, and bushes.

BLAM

BLAM

BLAM

BLAM

YOU REBEL COWARDS! COME OUT AND FIGHT LIKE REAL MEN!

At Lexington, the redcoats meet up with reinforcements, but it does them little good. As the British retreat back to Boston, the colonists pursue them, firing from cover and picking apart the British ranks. Nick follows, helping however he can.

NOW THERE'S THE BRAVEST SOLDIER IN THIS BATTLE TODAY.

IT'S DR. WARREN!

NICK, THANK GOD YOU'RE SAFE. COME, I NEED YOUR HELP WITH THE WOUNDED.

R-RIP

AAH!

I'M OKAY, JUST GRAZED. HELP ME CLEAN IT.

NICK, YOU HAVE A HEALING TOUCH.

BUT IT'S A SOLDIER I WANT TO BE.

As night falls, the British reach Charlestown on the shores of the river. The guns of their warships offer them protection as they're rowed back to Boston.

The patriots are jubilant.

WE SHOWED THEM WE AIN'T SCARED OF THEIR SLICK FORMATIONS AND FANCY UNIFORMS.

EASIER THAN SHOOTING WILD TURKEYS.

Dr. Warren and the other Committee of Safety members quickly set up a command headquarters in Cambridge.

GENTLEMEN, EVENTS HAVE OVERTAKEN US. OUR FIGHT FOR EQUALITY IS NOW AN OUTRIGHT WAR.

THERE ARE THOUSANDS OF VOLUNTEERS NOW FLOODING INTO THESE HILLS.

WE HAVE TO FIGURE OUT HOW TO FEED, SHELTER, EQUIP, AND PAY THEM. WE HAVE TO FIND LEADERS AMONG THEIR RANKS.

WE HAVE TO TURN THIS BUNCH OF UNRULY AMATEURS INTO A DISCIPLINED FIGHTING FORCE.

I OUTRANK YOU BECAUSE I'VE BEEN HERE A WEEK AND YOU ARRIVED ONLY TWO DAYS AGO!

MEANWHILE, WE TRY TO FIGURE OUT GENERAL GAGE'S NEXT MOVE.

NICK, WHERE ARE YOU GOING?

I'M GOING BACK TO LEXINGTON TO GET MAGGIE AND RETURN HER TO CHARLESTOWN.

THEN WHAT? BACK TO YOUR OLD OUTLAW LIFE IN BOSTON?

THAT LIFE IS OVER. I WANT TO STAY HERE AND BE A SOLDIER.

YOU'VE PROVEN YOU'VE GOT GUTS. NOW YOU NEED SOME TRAINING.

I'M GOING TO PUT YOU ON MY STAFF. YOU'LL CARRY MESSAGES, LEARN BASIC MEDICINE, AND BE MY EYES AND EARS AMONG THE MEN.

I'M READY! I'LL BE BACK TOMORROW.

YOU LOOK LIKE THERE'S SOMETHING ELSE ON YOUR MIND.

I WAS JUST THINKING ABOUT PENNY. I HOPE SHE'S ALL RIGHT.

CHAPTER 7

IN WHICH PENNY UNCOVERS A TRAITOR

The night of April 20, the Revere house.

TAP-TAP

RACHEL, IT'S ME, PAUL.

PAUL! WE'VE BEEN SO WORRIED!

I'M OKAY. SO ARE DR. WARREN, WILL BROWN, AND NICK. WE WON THE DAY AND OUR MILITIAS SURROUND BOSTON.

THE ORDER IS OUT FOR ALL OF OUR ARRESTS. I CAN'T RISK COMING INTO TOWN ANYMORE.

IT'S TERRIBLE HERE. THE SOLDIERS ARE TAKING OUT THEIR ANGER ON THE PEOPLE. EVERYONE IS RUNNING OUT OF FOOD AND FIREWOOD.

THE BRITISH WON'T PUT UP WITH THIS STANDOFF MUCH LONGER. THEY'LL BE COMING OUT AFTER US. WE JUST DON'T KNOW WHERE OR WHEN. I HAVE TO GET YOU ALL OUT OF HERE.

BUT HOW? YOU HAVE TO KNOW SOMEONE OR BRIBE A GUARD TO GET ACROSS THE NECK.

WARREN AND I WILL MAKE ARRANGEMENTS. WAIT FOR BILLY DAWES. HE'LL BE COMING INTO TOWN DISGUISED AS A FARMER.

DAWES WILL HAVE MONEY AND INSTRUCTIONS FOR YOU. WE'LL BE TOGETHER SOON.

GOD BE WITH YOU.

April 22.

PENNY, YOU SHOULDN'T BE OUT ON THE STREETS, IT'S DANGEROUS.

I NEED TO CHECK ON MY PARENTS' TAVERN. I'LL BE CAREFUL.

PEOPLE AFRAID IN THEIR OWN CITY. I DON'T RECOGNIZE BOSTON ANYMORE.

CRASH

OH!

NOTHING LEFT TO DRINK. WE'LL COME BACK LATER TO RIP OUT BEAMS FOR FIREWOOD.

HIC!

I'M GLAD MY PARENTS AREN'T HERE TO SEE THIS.

BROKEN BOTTLES EVERYWHERE.

Penny recognizes the voice of Dr. Church, who didn't believe Penny and Nick at the Committee of Safety meeting.

WE CAN MEET HERE. IT'S SAFE, THE OWNER IS ONE OF THE REBEL SCUM HIDING OUT IN CAMBRIDGE.

GENERAL GAGE IS PLEASED WITH YOUR INFORMATION. HERE'S YOUR PAYMENT.

THIS WILL KEEP MY WOMAN IN NEW FROCKS.

CRUNCH!

WHAT WAS THAT?!

!

I KNOW THAT GIRL!

YOU HAVE TO STOP HER!

DON'T WORRY. WE'LL SEND WORD TO THE GUARDS. SHE CAN'T GET OUT OF BOSTON.

A SPY FOR THE BRITISH! I HAVE TO TELL DR. WARREN. BUT NOW THEY'LL BE LOOKING FOR ME.

THAT FARMER TALKING TO MRS. REVERE...

...IT'S MR. DAWES. HE MADE IT!

MR. DAWES, IT'S ME, PENNY BROWN.

YUP, YUP.

I HAVE TO GET NEWS TO DR. WARREN—BUT THE BRITISH ARE LOOKING FOR ME.

IT WOULD BE EASIER IF YOU WERE A BOY. YOU COULD BE MY HELPER.

MRS. REVERE, I NEED YOUR HELP.

PAUL JR., SARAH. WE HAVE WORK TO DO!

20 minutes later.

MY CLOTHES LOOK BAGGY ON YOU. PRETEND YOU HAVE MUSCLES.

WALK WITH MORE SWAGGER, LIKE YOUR FRIEND NICK.

OKAY, MR. DAW— *WHOOPS!*

YUP, YUP. UP YOU GO! WE HAVE TO GET MOVING.

REMEMBER, PENNY, WHEN WE'RE IN FRONT OF THE GUARDS, YOU FOLLOW MY LEAD.

HOW SHOULD I ACT?

BOYISH! *GIDDAP THERE!*

CLOP CLOP CLOP

AND DON'T OPEN YOUR MOUTH OR WE'RE DEAD MEAT.

Boston Neck, the only land link between Boston and the mainland.

HERE WE GO.

HALT!

BOSTON NECK
MILITARY ZONE AHEAD
RESTRICTED PASSAGE

HOLD IT, FARMER! YOU WOULDN'T BE SMUGGLING GUNS OR REBELS OUT OF TOWN, WOULD YOU?

NOPE, NOPE.

OR MAYBE YOUR YOUNG HELPER IS CARRYING TOP SECRET MESSAGES.

GULP!

WHAP

HA, HA! GOOD JOKE, HUH, JEREMIAH?

I HAVE A GIFT FOR YOU GENTLEMEN—A BOTTLE OF BOSTON'S BEST RUM.

GIVE IT HERE AND BE ON YOUR WAY. NEXT TIME, *TWO* BOTTLES.

PENNY, WE'LL BE SAFELY BEHIND OUR LINES IN A MINUTE.

I THOUGHT WE WERE DOOMED!

YOU'RE AS GOOD AN ACTOR AS I AM, JEREMIAH.

NOW TO GET YOU TO DR. WARREN. *GIDDAP!*

Cambridge, temporary headquarters of the Boston rebellion.

WHAT DO YOU WANT, BOY... *PENNY?!?*

NICK! WHAT ARE YOU DOING HERE?

I'M WORKING FOR DR. WARREN. WHY ARE YOU DRESSED LIKE THAT? HOW'D YOU GET HERE?

LATER! FIRST, TAKE ME TO DR. WARREN. FAST!

Penny describes her encounter with Dr. Church to Dr. Warren.

CHURCH, A TRAITOR! I NEVER LIKED HIM, BUT I THOUGHT AT LEAST HE WAS A PATRIOT.

WE CAN'T ACCUSE HIM TILL WE HAVE HARD EVIDENCE. MEANWHILE, I'LL BE VERY CAREFUL WHAT'S SAID IN FRONT OF HIM.

FOR NOW, HE MUST NOT SUSPECT. IT'LL BE SAFER FOR YOU IF WE KEEP THIS BETWEEN US.

NOW, I'M SURE YOU WANT TO BE BACK WITH YOUR FAMILY.

NICK, TAKE THE CARRIAGE AND DRIVE HER TO BRAINTREE.

ACTUALLY, I...

NICK, I...

PENNY, I'M A REBEL SOLDIER NOW. OR I WILL BE WHEN I GET MY OWN MUSKET.

AND YOU'RE SORT OF LIKE A REAL SPY.

WHAT DO YOU MEAN "SORT OF"?! I *AM* A SPY, AND I'M NOT READY TO GO HOME.

SURE YOU ARE. SO, THERE I WAS AT THE BATTLE OF LEXINGTON...

WAIT! ME FIRST! WE WERE ALMOST CAUGHT AT BOSTON NECK...

CHAPTER 8

IN WHICH PENNY HIDES IN PLAIN SIGHT

On his way back from delivering messages to the Second Continental Congress in Philadelphia, Paul Revere stays overnight with Penny's family

MY FAMILY GOT OUT SAFELY—THANKS TO A COUPLE OF BRIBES IN THE RIGHT HANDS.

THEY'RE IN CAMBRIDGE FOR A FEW DAYS, BUT WILL BE LIVING IN WATERTOWN TILL WE CAN GET BACK INTO BOSTON.

I'LL BE RIDING BACK TO CAMBRIDGE EARLY IN THE MORNING.

At dawn the next morning.

MR. REVERE, CAN I RIDE BACK TO CAMBRIDGE WITH YOU? IT'S OKAY WITH MY PARENTS.

WELL, SURE. YOU CAN STAY WITH US UNTIL WE LEAVE.

MOM, DAD, I'VE GONE BACK TO CAMBRIDGE. THIS FIGHT IS MY FIGHT, TOO. I PROMISE TO BE CAREFUL. LOVE, PENNY

Later that day

NICK, I'M BACK!

I KNEW YOU COULDN'T STAY AWAY FROM ME.

HILARIOUS. SO WHAT'S GOING ON?

OUR OFFICERS HAVE BEEN TRYING TO TURN CIVILIANS INTO SOLDIERS, WHICH IS HARD WHEN THEY CAN'T EVEN UNDERSTAND EACH OTHER'S ACCENTS.

WE KEEP HEARING RUMORS OF A NEW BRITISH ATTACK, AND OF TOUGH GENERALS ARRIVING FROM ENGLAND TO TAKE OVER FROM GAGE.

DR. WARREN SAYS IF ONLY WE HAD SOMEONE INSIDE THE BOSTON CAMP TO GET RELIABLE INFORMATION.

NICK, I'M GOING BACK TO BOSTON.

ARE YOU CRAZY?!

I'LL POSE AS A TORY SERVANT GIRL. I'LL TRY TO GET WORK IN A BRITISH HOME AND MAYBE HEAR SOMETHING.

ABSOLUTELY NOT! IT'S TOO RISKY!

YOU'RE NOT THE BOSS OF ME. THIS IS MY COUNTRY TOO, YOU KNOW!

BUT YOU'RE A *GIRL!*

EXACTLY, YOU DOPE. NOBODY WILL NOTICE A LITTLE SERVANT GIRL.

THE QUESTION IS, HOW DO I GET BACK INTO TOWN?

YOU'LL NEVER MAKE IT. THE NECK IS JAMMED WITH TORIES TRYING TO GET TO BRITISH PROTECTION IN BOSTON.

THAT'S IT! I'LL SAY MY MASTER'S HOUSE WAS BURNED DOWN BY A REBEL MOB, AND I'M LOOKING FOR WORK IN BOSTON.

WAIT A MINUTE! WE HAVE TO TALK THIS OVER WITH DR. WARREN.

DON'T YOU DARE TELL HIM TILL AFTER I'M GONE. I'M GOING TO FIND SOME SERVANT'S CLOTHES.

One hour later, Penny tries out her new role on Nick.

GOOD DAY, SIR. SALLY BAKER, OUT-OF-WORK SERVANT GIRL, AT YOUR SERVICE.

I GOTTA SAY, YOU'RE A NATURAL SCULLERY MAID.

WE NEED TO KNOW YOU'RE SAFE. I'LL ROW ACROSS ONCE A WEEK, AND YOU CAN PASS ME ANY INFORMATION.

HOW ABOUT WE MEET AT THE BURIAL GROUNDS ON THE HILL ABOVE OLD NORTH CHURCH? I'LL SNEAK OUT ON SUNDAY WHEN EVERYONE'S AT CHURCH.

I'LL PRETEND I'M FISHING AND BRINGING MY FRESH CATCH TO THE BRITISH. I'LL WAIT FOR YOU IN THE CEMETERY.

Penny hikes to the Neck and joins the line of Tories struggling with children and property.

HERE, LET ME HELP YOU WITH YOUR CHILD.

IT'S SO NICE TO MEET A WELL-MANNERED TORY, NOT LIKE THE VILE REBELS OUT HERE.

I KNOW WHAT YOU MEAN, MA'AM.

NEXT! HAVE YOUR PAPERS READY.

Once in Boston, Penny heads for the big homes around British headquarters and, posing as a good Tory begins knocking on doors, looking for work.

NO! WE DON'T TRUST STRANGERS!

SLAM

WE HAVE TWO SLAVES—THEY DO ALL THE WORK.

SLAM

WE'VE HAD TO LET SERVANTS GO. TIMES ARE HARD.

SLAM

PLEASE, I'M STRONG, A HARD WORKER— I'LL DO ANYTHING.

YOU LOOK KINDA SCRAWNY.

AH, I'LL TAKE A CHANCE. I HAVE TO ADD TO MY STAFF. A NEW GENERAL IS ARRIVING SHORTLY FROM LONDON AND HE WILL BE STAYING HERE.

THE HOUSE MUST BE SPOTLESS FOR GENERAL BURGOYNE. YOU WILL WORK WITH COOK. BEGIN BY SCRUBBING THE KITCHEN FLOOR.

YES, MA'AM. THANK YOU, MA'AM.

Ugh.

One week later, Penny has learned nothing.

OINK OINK

THANK YOU, GENERAL FAT PIG, I'LL GET THAT INFORMATION TO NICK RIGHT AWAY.

WHEN THE GENERAL ARRIVES, YOU STAY OUT OF SIGHT—OR YOU'LL END UP IN COOK'S MINCE PIE.

OH, GREAT. NICK, WHY DID YOU TALK ME INTO THIS?

GENERAL GAGE'S MAID SAYS GENERAL BURGOYNE AND TWO OTHERS ARE COMING TO LEAD AN ATTACK AGAINST THE REBELS.

FINALLY, SOME REAL INFORMATION!

May 25, 1775.

THE GENERAL ARRIVES TODAY, BUT THE SHIP BRINGING HIS WINE FROM PORTUGAL IS DELAYED!

WHAT ARE WE GOING TO DO?! *THE GENERAL MUST HAVE HIS WINE!*

EXCUSE ME, MA'AM.

NOT NOW!

BUT I KNOW WHERE TO FIND SOME MADEIRA.

WHAT?! HOW COULD YOU...? NEVER MIND.

I DON'T WANT TO KNOW ABOUT YOUR SHADY DEALS WITH THIEVING LOWLIFES.

JUST FETCH IT QUICKLY!

IF IT'S BAD, I WILL HAVE YOU CLEANING OUT EVERY PRIVY IN THE NEIGHBORHOOD.

GO!

AND IF IT'S GOOD?

IF IT'S NOT THERE...

...I'M IN SERIOUS TROUBLE.

YES!

HERE, MA'AM. TWO BOTTLES.

QUICK, GIVE 'EM TO ME. HE JUST ARRIVED, AND HE WANTS HIS WINE!

General "Gentleman Johnny" Burgoyne spends his first night in the Colonies.

AHH, A PERFECT WELCOME AFTER A ROUGH MONTH AT SEA—IF IT'S ANY GOOD.

SMACK!

GOOD COLOR, TANGY CARAMEL FLAVOR, SLIGHTLY SWEET...EXCELLENT.

WE NEED MORE BOTTLES.

AND I NEED TO BE PROMOTED. I WANT TO SERVE THE GENERAL.

YOU LITTLE BLACKMAILER!

FINE, GET THE MADEIRA AND YOU'RE IN. BUT IF YOU MESS UP, YOU'LL BE PIG FOOD BY MORNING.

NOW, GO MAKE ME LOOK GOOD OR...

I KNOW. YOU'LL ROAST ME AND SERVE ME FOR DINNER.

Over the next few days, "Sally Baker" works her way into the favor of General Burgoyne.

THANK YOU, SALLY.

Saturday June 10. General Burgoyne calls his senior staff together for a council of war. Penny serves—and listens.

IT HAS BEEN DECIDED: FIRST AN ASSAULT ON DORCHESTER HEIGHTS...

...THEN WE ATTACK CAMBRIDGE...

...AND MOVE ON TO CHARLESTOWN...

...AND BUNKER HILL.

WE BEGIN ON SUNDAY, JUNE 18. THEY'LL NEVER EXPECT AN ATTACK ON THE LORD'S DAY.

SECRECY IS ESSENTIAL. THIS WILL NOT BECOME ANOTHER LEXINGTON AND CONCORD.

SALLY! MADEIRA ALL AROUND. WE WILL TOAST OUR FORTHCOMING VICTORY AGAINST THESE PEASANTS!

YES, SIR.

Sunday morning, June 11. Penny has been in Boston for more than a month. Nick has rowed across every Sunday but he hasn't seen her yet

DON'T KNOW HOW MANY MORE SUNDAYS I CAN GET AWAY WITH THIS BEFORE SOME SHORELINE GUARD GETS SUSPICIOUS.

Copp's Hill Burial Ground.

BONG, BONG, BONG...

THE CHURCH BELLS. PLEASE, PENNY, BE HERE.

PLEASE, NICK, BE HERE.

WHAT IF SHE'S HURT?

WHAT IF HE CAN'T GET ACROSS?

UH-OH! BRITISH SOLDIERS SURROUNDING MY BOAT. BETTER GET OUT OF HERE.

THE NECK GUARDED, THE SHORE PATROLLED. SOLDIERS EVERYWHERE.

I KNOW EVERY STREET AND ALLEY OF THIS TOWN.

BUT I DON'T KNOW HOW TO GET OUT.

YUCK! WHAT'S THAT AWFUL SMELL?!?

IT'S THE NIGHT-WASTE CART.

IT DUMPS THE CONTENTS OF BOSTON'S PRIVIES INTO...

YEOW!

GAAGH!

GAAGH!

MONSTER!

TIME FOR A SWIM.

Avoiding British eyes, Nick dog-paddles across the Charles.

CHAPTER 9

IN WHICH NICK JOINS THE BATTLE AND LOSES A FRIEND

Cambridge, June 11.

DR. WARREN, PENNY IS FINE, AND I HAVE HER REPORT.

WONDERFUL, NICK. BUT GET OUTSIDE— YOU *STINK.*

NICK, PENNY'S INFORMATION IS CRUCIAL! WE MUST CALL AN EMERGENCY MEETING...

...OF THE COMMITTEE OF SAFETY.

BUT FIRST, GO TELL DR. CHURCH TO COME TO MY OFFICE. THEN YOU TAKE A BATH.

DR. CHURCH, I NEED YOU TO TAKE THESE DISPATCHES TO...

...ADAMS AND HANCOCK AT THE CONTINENTAL CONGRESS IN PHILADELPHIA.

WHAT?!

BUT, WARREN, I'M ESSENTIAL HERE! THESE ARE CRITICAL TIMES.

EXACTLY.

THESE DOCUMENTS ARE TOO VALUABLE TO ENTRUST TO ANYONE ELSE.

!@#$%!

WITH CHURCH GONE, WE CAN BE SURE OUR PLANS WON'T END UP IN BRITISH HANDS.

I'M GOING TO RECOMMEND THAT THE WAY TO UPSET THE BRITISH PLANS IS TO *BEAT THEM TO THE PUNCH!*

BUT, SIR, YOU SAY OUR OFFICERS ARE UNTESTED, WE'RE SHORT OF SUPPLIES AND EQUIPMENT...

...AND SOME OF THE SOLDIERS' MUSKETS GO BACK TO THEIR GRANDFATHERS' DAY.

TRUE, NICK, BUT THERE'S ONE THING I'M SURE OF: IF THE BRITISH THINK...

...THE COURAGE WE SHOWED AT LEXINGTON AND CONCORD WAS A FLUKE, THEY'RE IN FOR A SHOCK!

KABLAM

THERE'S ANOTHER THING I'M SURE OF...

WHAT'S THAT, SIR?

YOU STILL SMELL. INTO THE RIVER AGAIN—THIS TIME, USE HORSE SOAP.

I'M ON IT, SIR.

THEN IT'S AGREED, WE SECRETLY OCCUPY BUNKER HILL TOMORROW NIGHT.

WHEN THE BRITISH GENERALS WAKE UP SATURDAY MORNING, THE SIGHT OF US WILL HIT THEM RIGHT BETWEEN THE EYES.

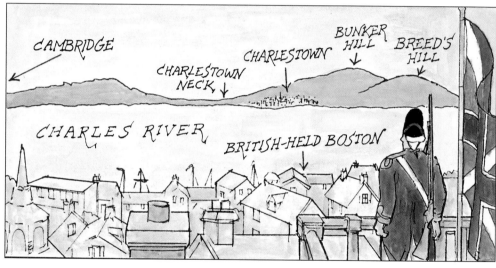

CAMBRIDGE

CHARLESTOWN NECK

CHARLESTOWN

BUNKER HILL

BREED'S HILL

CHARLES RIVER

BRITISH-HELD BOSTON

DR. WARREN, I WANT TO MARCH WITH THE TROOPS.

NICK, I CANNOT TELL YOU NO.

MANY HAVE TOLD ME MY JOB IS RIGHT HERE.

BUT I, TOO, FEEL MY PLACE IS ON THAT HILL...

...EVEN IF I DIE THERE.

June 16, morning.

NICK, COLONEL PRESCOTT WILL BE LEADING OUR FORCES TONIGHT. HE'S A GOOD MAN. I WISH WE HAD MORE LIKE HIM.

HE HAS AGREED TO TAKE YOU ON AS AN ADJUTANT. I TOLD HIM YOU ARE BRAVE AND RESOURCEFUL...

...IF SOMETIMES A BIT TOO DARING.

GATHER A DAY'S PROVISIONS AND REPORT TO HIM RIGHT AWAY.

WOOHOO!

June 16, dusk. Nick reports to Colonel Prescott.

STAY NEAR AND ALERT, NICK, THIS WILL BE A LONG NIGHT, WITH PLENTY FOR YOU TO DO.

PASS THE WORD DOWN THE RANKS: WE ARE 1,000 MEN, AND WE MUST SOUND LIKE 1,000 SHADOWS.

June 16, 7 p.m. The troops set out from Cambridge, heading for Bunker Hill.

CLANK
CLATTER
MUTTER
SHUFFLE
GRUNT
SHHHH!

Crossing Charlestown Neck.

ANYONE KNOW WHERE WE'RE HEADING?

I HEARD BUNKER HILL.

WHAT'S THE PLAN?

TRY TO STAY ALIVE.

Once past the Neck, Prescott orders a halt and confers with two officers.

LOOKS LIKE THEY'RE ARGUING.

NOT A GOOD SIGN.

STILL TIME FOR YOU TO GET OUT, NICK.

I'M STAYING.

Finally the meeting ends, and the columns march on through the black night.

NICK, NOTIFY COMPANY COMMANDERS: FROM NOW ON, COMPLETE SILENCE!

SHUT UP!

WHEREVER WE ARE, I CAN HEAR BRITISH SENTRIES OVER IN BOSTON.

WHICH HILL?

WE'RE CLIMBING SOME HILL.

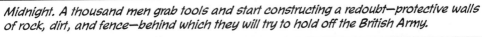

Midnight. A thousand men grab tools and start constructing a redoubt—protective walls of rock, dirt, and fence—behind which they will try to hold off the British Army.

CRUNCH

QUIET!

WE HAVE TO SHOVEL!

SHOVEL QUIETER.

AND FASTER.

!@#9%!

June 17, Breed's Hill, 4 a.m.

HEY, I CAN MAKE OUT SHAPES.

WAIT A MINUTE! WE'RE ON *THE WRONG HILL!*

THIS AIN'T BUNKER HILL, IT'S *BREED'S HILL.*

WE'RE EVEN *MORE* EXPOSED TO BRITISH FIRE.

1:30 p.m. The weary rebels drop their shovels and grab their guns. Long lines of barges stream toward them, the elite British troops landing on the beach below Breed's Hill.

BOOM! BOOM! BOOM! BOOM! BOOM!

MY GOD! MUST BE OVER 1,500 OF 'EM. GUESS WE GOT THEIR ATTENTION.

NICK, CHECK ON CAPTAIN KNOWLTON ON OUR LEFT FLANK. THEN MAKE SURE CAPTAIN GRIDLEY HAS HIS CANNONS IN POSITION.

HOW ARE YOU DOING, CAPTAIN KNOWLTON?

WE HAVE A BIT OF STONE, FENCE, AND STRAW AS PROTECTION. THAT'S ALL WE NEED. *NO ONE'S GETTING THROUGH US!*

BOOM!

CAPTAIN GRIDLEY, WHERE ARE YOU GOING?

ANYWHERE BUT HERE!

COLONEL PRESCOTT— KNOWLTON'S MEN ARE DUG IN AND READY. BUT CAPTAIN GRIDLEY IS RUNNING AWAY WITH HIS CANNONS.

THAT COWARD! KNOWLTON *NEEDS* THOSE CANNONS. TAKE THIS MUSKET AND GET THEM BACK!

June 17, 2 p.m.

COLONEL PRESCOTT, HERE ARE TWO CANNONS AND THE BRAVE ARTILLERYMEN WHO WILL FIRE THEM.

BOOM!

GOOD MEN! NICK, TAKE THEM OVER TO CAPTAIN KNOWLTON, AND THEN...

...AND THEN GET INTO THE FRONT LINE MYSELF?

NO. GIVE ME THE MUSKET. I HAVE MORE IMPORTANT WORK FOR YOU.

I NEED YOU TO GO UP AND DOWN THE LINES, MAKING SURE EVERYONE HAS HIS SHARE OF AMMUNITION...

BOOM!

...AND TELL EVERYONE TO STAY BEHIND THEIR BARRIERS—*NO MATTER WHAT!*

YES, SIR.

GOT A PLACE FOR ME, PRESCOTT?

DR. WARREN! WILL YOU TAKE COMMAND, SIR?

I'M HERE AS A VOLUNTEER. PUT ME IN THE LINE WHERE I CAN BE MOST USEFUL.

STRATEGY?! DON'T FIRE UNTIL YOU SEE THE WHITES OF THEIR EYES. AIM FOR THEIR OFFICERS. FIRE LOW....*PRETEND THEY'RE WILD TURKEYS!*

NICK, SPREAD THE WORD, NO FIRING TILL I GIVE THE OKAY.

SIR, LOOK AT THEM—GETTING *SO CLOSE I CAN ALMOST COUNT THEIR BUTTONS.*

GOOD! *HOLD FIRE, HOLD FIRE...*

...*HOLD, HOLD...*

...NOW, *FIRE!*

BAM!
BAM!
BAM!
BAM!
BAM!
BAM!

AGHH!
OOOF!
ARGH!
AAH!
AHG!
UGH!
GAH!

The devastating rebel fire tears apart the front line of British soldiers. As the bodies crumple, the second line moves up and it, too, is hit by ferocious fire. Some colonials fall, but the bodies of dying and wounded redcoats cover the field.

WE'VE BROKEN THEIR LINES!

THEY'RE TURNING...

...RETREATING...

...RUNNING!

WE'VE WON!

WE'VE BEATEN THE LEGENDARY BRITISH INFANTRY.

NO. THEY'RE REGROUPING.

MEN, YOU'VE SHOWN GREAT COURAGE, BUT DO NOT FALTER NOW—THIS FIGHT IS FAR FROM OVER.

The British lines advance once more, stepping over the bodies of their comrades, firing as they get close. Again the rebels let loose a barrage, and the British are driven back.

WHAT DO YOU THINK OF YOUR YANKEE YOKELS NOW?

THEY WON'T ATTACK AGAIN.

JUST AS WELL. I'M ALMOST OUT OF AMMUNITION.

ME TOO.

I HAVE FIVE CARTRIDGES LEFT.

UH-OH! FRESH REINFORCEMENTS ARE ARRIVING. THE REDCOATS ARE PREPARING A THIRD ASSAULT.

MEN, LOOK FOR NAILS AND SCRAP METAL—ANYTHING THAT CAN BE SHOT FROM A MUSKET.

EVERYONE WHO CAN PULL A TRIGGER GET UP ON THE LINE.

THIS SOLDIER HAS BEEN KILLED. HELP ME MOVE HIM OFF THIS BATTLEMENT. YES.

HE WAS A BRAVE MAN. MAY HE REST IN PEACE.

I'LL TAKE HIS MUSKET AND HIS PLACE IN LINE AND TRY TO BE AS BRAVE.

HERE THEY COME—IN COLUMNS THIS TIME! DOESN'T MATTER—NO LACK OF TARGETS.

Sunset. Once more, the battered British soldiers march relentlessly up through the bloody debris on Breed's Hill into a wall of rebel fire.

BAM! BAM! BAM! BAM! BAM! BAM! BAM! BAM! BAM! BAM! BAM! BAM!

The rebels are on the verge of crushing the British when their ammunition gives out. Maddened redcoats reach the barricades and scramble over, slashing with bayonets.

THWACK!

AAH!

WE CAN'T HOLD THEM BACK!

RETREAT! COVER EACH OTHER! GET OUT AS BEST YOU CAN!

FALL BACK ACROSS CHARLESTOWN NECK!

DR. WARREN, WE HAVE TO GET OUT OF HERE!

GO ON, NICK! THOSE OF US WITH A LITTLE AMMUNITION WILL STAY BACK AND PROTECT THE WITHDRAWAL.

BAM!

The weary and wounded rebels retreat across Charlestown Neck. Nick, still in shock, is among them. The British, in disarray and suffering horrific casualties, cannot follow.

HEY, SOLDIER, I KNOW YOU. YOU WERE NEXT TO ME ON THE BATTLEMENTS.

YOU'RE BLEEDING BADLY. SIT DOWN, LET ME TAKE A LOOK.

BUT...

DON'T WORRY, I WORKED FOR A DOCTOR. WE HAVE TO PUT PRESSURE ON THAT WOUND.

DO YOU HAVE FAR TO GO?

I BOUGHT MY FREEDOM BY JOINING THIS FIGHT. THE ARMY IN CAMBRIDGE IS MY HOME NOW.

I NEED SOME CLEAN CLOTH TO PACK YOUR WOUND.

HERE, USE THIS.

THANKS.

YOU'RE WELCOME. IT'S A PIECE OF MY PETTICOAT.

PENNY! HOW'D YOU GET HERE?

WHEN THE FIGHTING STARTED, THERE WAS SUCH CHAOS IN TOWN, I WAS ABLE TO SLIP OUT.

WHEN I COULDN'T FIND YOU OR DR. WARREN IN CAMBRIDGE, I KEPT WALKING AND WALKING.

PENNY, DR. WARREN IS DEAD.

OH, NICK.

THERE. THAT'LL HOLD YOU TILL YOU GET BACK TO CAMBRIDGE.

THANK YOU, DOCTOR.

I'M SO SORRY.

SO MUCH HAS HAPPENED.

YOU LOOK TERRIBLE, YOU KNOW.

YOU DON'T LOOK SO HOT YOURSELF.

DR. WARREN SAID HIS PLACE WAS ON THE HILL—EVEN IF HE DIED THERE. BUT I NEVER THOUGHT...

I WANT TO HEAR EVERYTHING.

YOU WILL. BUT LET'S GET BACK TO CAMBRIDGE. I WANT TO PICK UP SOME OF DR. WARREN'S SUPPLIES AND HELP WITH THE WOUNDED.

MY PETTICOATS WILL MAKE LOTS OF GOOD BANDAGES.

CHAPTER 10

IN WHICH PENNY AND NICK ARE SUMMONED
TO AN IMPORTANT MEETING

Following the battle on Breed's Hill, both sides face the grim fact that war between the British Empire and her American colonies has truly begun.

DON'T GET CAPTURED. I HEAR THEY'LL MAKE YOU WATCH YOUR OWN INSIDES BEING TORN OUT.

Nick honors Dr. Warren's memory by assisting Dr. Warren's brother, John, an army doctor.

Appointed by the Second Continental Congress, General George Washington of Virginia arrives in Cambridge to take command of the new Continental Army—which now includes Nick.

BIG, ISN'T HE!

WHERE'S VIRGINIA?

MEN, YOU HAVE PROVEN YOUR VALOR. I NOW INTEND TO TURN YOU INTO A DISCIPLINED FIGHTING FORCE.

HEY, NICK. WHAT'S HE MEAN BY THAT?

I THINK HE WANTS US TO MARCH IN FORMATION LIKE THE BRITISH.

NO WAY! WHAT'S THAT GOT TO DO WITH KILLING REDCOATS?

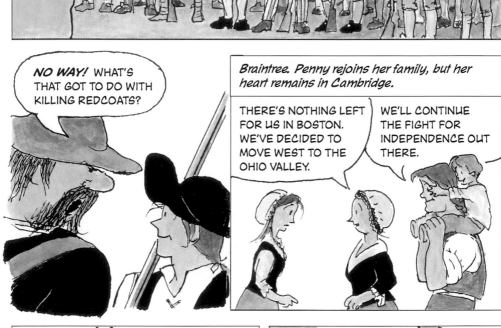

Braintree. Penny rejoins her family, but her heart remains in Cambridge.

THERE'S NOTHING LEFT FOR US IN BOSTON. WE'VE DECIDED TO MOVE WEST TO THE OHIO VALLEY.

WE'LL CONTINUE THE FIGHT FOR INDEPENDENCE OUT THERE.

JUST THINK, PENNY, IT'LL BE AN ADVENTURE.

THIS IS A COUNTRY FULL OF OPPORTUNITY FOR THOSE BRAVE ENOUGH TO TAKE THE RISK.

BUT THERE ARE RISKS I HAVE TO TAKE FIRST.

Cambridge.

PENNY, I THOUGHT YOU WERE WITH YOUR FAMILY.

THEY'RE PLANNING TO MOVE WEST. I TOLD THEM MY PLACE IS HERE.

WHAT DID THEY SAY?

THEY ARGUED WITH ME. MY FATHER USED HIS FIRM VOICE. BUT EVENTUALLY THEY AGREED AND SAID THEY WERE PROUD OF ME.

I JUST CAME FROM COLONEL PRESCOTT. I TOLD HIM I'M GOING TO BE PART OF THIS, EVEN IF I HAVE TO...

...COOK AND CLEAN. HE SAID HE HAD SOMETHING IN MIND FOR ME.

PENELOPE BROWN AND NICHOLAS?

NICHO... OH, RIGHT, THAT'S ME.

YES?

YOU ARE ORDERED TO APPEAR BEFORE GENERAL WASHINGTON *IMMEDIATELY!*

NOW WHAT DID YOU DO?

MAYBE I'M GETTING A MEDAL.

FOLLOW ME, PLEASE.

114

PENELOPE, I'M TOLD YOU'RE AN EXCELLENT SCULLERY MAID AND WAITRESS...

UH...

HEH.

...AND SPY. I'D LIKE YOU TO SERVE IN THE CONTINENTAL ARMY AS AN UNDERCOVER AGENT.

IT WOULD BE INVALUABLE TO US TO HAVE A SPY AMONG THE TORIES OF THE NEW YORK COLONY.

WE HAVE AN AGENT THERE WHO RUNS A TAVERN THAT CATERS TO THE BRITISH. YOU'LL WORK FOR HIM.

UNDERSTAND THAT I AM ASKING YOU TO RUN GREAT RISKS. *DO YOU NEED TIME TO THINK THIS OVER?*

NO, SIR. WE'RE READY!

HE MAKES ME BELIEVE I CAN DO ANYTHING.

DID YOU NOTICE HOW HE SMILED AT ME? THE GENERAL AND I ARE LIKE *THAT.*

Fall, 1775. The Americans intercept a secret coded letter from Dr. Benjamin Church intended for British officials. Dr. Church is put on trial and convicted of treachery.

DR. CHURCH, WE FIND YOU GUILTY OF SPYING FOR THE BRITISH.

I AM INNOCENT. NO ONE HAS MORE LOVE FOR THE LIBERTIES OF AMERICA THAN I.

Nick and Penny, along with Rachel and Paul Revere, watch the proceedings.

THESE ARE TRUMPED-UP CHARGES.

I WISH DR. WARREN COULD BE HERE TO SEE THIS.

Early in 1776. Penny's and Nick's paths now diverge. Penny will infiltrate the Tory world of New York City. Nick will be put to the test as a doctor in the Battle of Long Island.

I FEEL SO MUCH OLDER THAN WHEN WE FIRST MET—BACK WHEN YOU WERE A THIEF.

AND YOU WERE SUCH A PROPER GIRL.

EPILOGUE

IN WHICH WE LEARN WHAT'S FACT AND WHAT'S FICTION

CHAPTER 1

Penny and Nick are fictional but...

* Girls and boys *did* work as spies for the patriot cause.
* Sarah Revere, then age twelve (and her brother Paul Revere, Jr., fifteen, and stepmother Rachel Revere), were all real people.

CHAPTER 2

Nick may be showing off when he takes a swig of Madeira, but...

* It was very common for everyone—including kids—to drink alcohol because the water supply in town was not safe, and even milk was potentially contaminated.

CHAPTER 3

Penny didn't yell "Fire!" in Old South Meeting House, but...

* British soldiers *were* planning to arrest the rebel leaders if Warren's talk became treasonous. (One story is that a soldier was planning to drop a raw egg as the signal to the other soldiers—but the egg broke on the way to Old South!) According to an account of the event, while Samuel Adams was talking, British soldiers yelled "Fie!" (meaning, "You lie!"), which someone in the crowd heard as "Fire!" and there was a stampede as everyone rushed out of the meetinghouse.

CHAPTER 4

Penny didn't overhear the British officers in the stable, but...

* It is believed that a young stablehand *did* pass that information along to the Committee of Safety

Nick didn't light the lanterns in Old North Church, but..

* Sexton Robert Newman is real, and he *did* light the lanterns along with John Pulling. Newman was later thrown in jail—and John Pulling had to hide in a wine barrel to escape the soldiers who were looking for him.

CHAPTER 5
Nick and Will Brown didn't row Paul Revere across the Charles, but..

* Two friends of Paul Revere *did*—and there's a legend that it was the girlfriend of one of them who provided the petticoat to muffle the oarlock.

CHAPTER 6
Nick didn't ride out to Lexington and get stopped by British soldiers, but..

* Paul Revere *was* stopped by soldiers while on his way to Concord. When he told them the countryside was preparing to fight, the soldiers released him and rushed to alert the redcoats coming from Boston.

CHAPTER 7
Penny didn't spot Dr. Church taking money from the British but..

* Church *was* a spy and a double-crosser. Once, when Paul Revere asked Church to get money from Rachel Revere and bring it to him, Church instead gave the money and Rachel's letter to British General Gage (we know this because Rachel's letter was found years later among Gage's personal papers). Dr. Church's court martial in the fall of 1775 took place as described in the book.

Billy Dawes may not have smuggled Penny Brown out of Boston, but..

* He did sneak in and out of town disguised as a farmer—often a drunken one!

CHAPTER 8
Penny didn't overhear the British plans to attack Bunker Hill, but..

* Some historians believe that the intelligence was passed on to the patriots by none other than General Gage's American-born wife, Margaret.

We doubt anyone ever hid in a wagon full of you-know-what to get out of town, but..

*   There really were "night waste" men who had the thrilling job of cleaning out all the privies (outhouses) in town.

CHAPTER 9
Even if Nick wasn't really at the Battle of Bunker Hill...
*   All the officers mentioned in the book were real—including the cowardly Captain Gridley who ran away from the battle.
*   History refers to the conflict as the Battle of Bunker Hill, although Breed's Hill is the spot where the actual fighting took place.
*   Many African Americans and Native Americans fought on Bunker Hill and throughout the Revolution.
*   Tragically, Dr. Warren was killed on Bunker Hill. He was thirty-four years old. Had he lived, he would undoubtedly have been one of the major leaders of the Revolution—and might have been as well known today as George Washington or Samuel Adams.

CHAPTER 10
The war between England and the colonies would ultimately spread from Canada down to Georgia, and Washington did lead major battles in New York, including Brooklyn and Long Island. The war ended in 1781—guess who won?!

All the principles that the patriots fought for were embodied in the Declaration of Independence, the Constitution, and the Bill of Rights. These ideas—that all people are created equal, that government serves the people, and that citizens have important rights that can't be taken away—were so important to the colonists that they were willing to die for them. We can't ever take these privileges for granted.

ACKNOWLEDGMENTS

If you're going to have your fictional characters engage in the events of history, you'd better make sure you know your history. The following people provided great assistance in helping us get our facts straight (any errors that remain are entirely our own): Gretchen G. Adams and Patrick M. Leehey, Paul Revere House, Boston; Martin Blatt, Ph.D., Sheila Cooke-Kayser, and Phil Hunt, Boston National Historical Park; Ed Pignone and Keara O'Leary, Old North Church; Steve Cole, Buckman Tavern, Lexington Common; Edwin Page, medical historian; Tom and Mary Jo Benjamin; Kate Sullivan.

We're also grateful to several people who helped make sure our book would please the toughest critics of all—the kids who will read it and the educators who teach American history: Stan Brimberg and his seventh-grade class at the Bank Street School, New York; Brent Beaty, Eagle Rock High School, Los Angeles; Jill Davis; Matthew Cecconi; Marsha Miller; Mariana Serra.